Bunch of fun!
Cool
Always happy
Style icon
Super sweet
Cheeky
Smart
Fabulous

SHOPKINS: ANNUAL 2019

A CENTUM BOOK 9781912564453

Published in Great Britain by Centum Books Ltd

This edition published 2018

1 3 5 7 9 10 8 6 4 2

Centum Books Ltd, 20 Devon Square, Newton Abbot, Devon TQ12 2HR, UK

books@centumbooksltd.co.uk

CENTUM BOOKS Limited Reg. No. 07641486

A CIP catalogue record for this book is available from the British Library.

Printed in Italy

This SHOPKINS™ book belongs to:

____

centum

WHAT'S INSIDE?

Puzzles

P8 Puzzles
P11 Chatter-phones
P12 Puzzles
P15 Selfie the Difference
P18 Puzzles
P19 Friendship Group Search
P25 Puzzles
P28 Mall Maze
P34 Puzzles
P42 The Friendship Parade
P43 Parade Maze
P44 Puzzles
P50 Friendship Words
P52 Puzzles
P60 Puzzles
P68 Puzzles
P70 Puzzles
P71 Pippa Puzzle
P72 The Name Game
P73 Wild Style Memories

Games

P10 Colourful Friends
P13 Who's Coming to Play?
P14 The Friendship Time Game
P16 Fruit and Friends
P17 Buncho's Squares Game
P24 Name Tags
P27 Colourful Celebration
P30 Colour and Collect
P33 Create Your Own Shoppie
P35 Friend of the Week
P40 The Race to Small Mart
P45 Parade of Colour
P51 Pixel Pals
P62 Color Change Cuties
P63 Tribe Search
P66 Chill Out and Colour In

P20 Story Time
P26 Friends Forever Quiz
P32 Friendship Calculator
P36 Storybook Writer
P46 Best Friend Selfie Mobile
P54 Meet The Wild Style Tribes
P64 Which Tribe Are You?
P67 Tribe Talking
P74 Check Ya Later!
P79 Posters

IT'S SHOPKINS TIME!

Calling all friends of Shopkins... it's me, Strawberry Kiss! Welcome to Shopville! All my friends from the Small Mart say "hi!" and hope you have fun looking through our new, shop-tastic book! We've packed it full of awesome puzzles, glamorous games, cool crafts, super quizzes and lots and lots of Shopkins fun!

We hope you make lots of new BFFs along the way, and remember to say "Hello!" to all your old favourites. The Shoppies are back with lots of shop-til-you-drop fun and there are some new wild and wonderful tribes in town for you to meet!

ARE YOU READY? C'MON, LET'S GO SHOPPING!

Hi! Sneaky Wedge here! I've got a fun game to get the SPK fun started! Inside your super-fab Shopkins Annual, I've hidden a couple of old friends. As you look through, see if you can find them. Remember to tick them off as you spot them!

TOASTY POP

CHEE ZEE

BREAKY CRUNCH

ROCKIN' BROC

NUTTY BUTTER

BESTIES PAIR-UP GAME

The Shopkins are playing a game at Miss Pressy's Friendship Party! Each Shopkin has chosen two things they love. Can you pair up the Shopkins to their perfect friend by matching their favourite things?

CHEEKY'S NEW BFF

Cheeky Chocolate has a brand-new, super-sweet best friend! Can you work out who it is? Cross out the letter pairs below and then solve the anagram with the remaining letters!

_ _ _ E _ T _ _ _

DANCE PARTNERS

It's time to dance! The Shopkins have paired up and are dancing the night away at the Friendship Party. Using the close-up photos, can you work out the Shopkins dance partnerships?

A

B

C

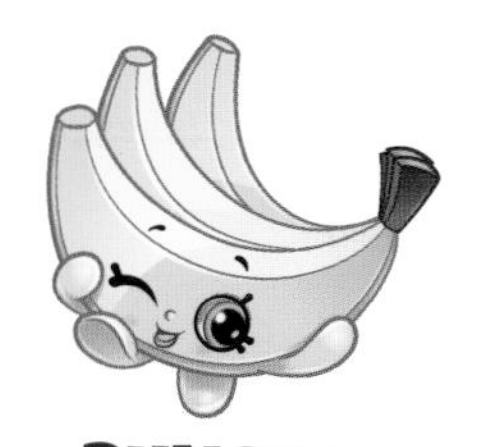

BUNCHO BANANAS

CHEEZEY B.

LIPPY LIPS

SODA POPS

PIPPA LEMON

APPLE BLOSSOM

PARTY BAG TANGLE

Hi, I'm Miss Pressy!
I hope you enjoyed my Friendship Party! My Shopkins friends loved it! But now they are all tired and need to go home. Can you help me untangle them to see which party bag belongs to each Shopkin!

Answers on page 75

COLOURFUL FRIENDS

Miss Pressy and Cheeky Chocolate had a fantastic time at the Friendship Party and now want to chill out and look colourful!

CHATTER-PHONES

Help D'lish connect friends on the Shopville telephone exchange by cracking the phone dials below then drawing a line between the matching Shopkins.

Solve the phone dials by crossing out the first number on each wheel, then every other number to discover the phone number. Now match the phone number to the Shopkins' phones below.

Answers on page 75

WHICH KOOKY?

Sneaky Wedge is having a play date with her best friend Kooky Cookie! Help her work out which is the 'real' Kooky by spotting the odd one out!

THE GUESS ME GAME

Sneaky and Kooky are playing a fun guessing game. Can you help them guess the Shopkin by reading the clues?

1. I'm a HOLE lot of fun to be ROUND!
2. I'm a pink, super-sweet best friend!
3. I love dressing up in sprinkles!

?

Use the Shopkin's shadow as an extra clue!

WHO'S COMING TO PLAY?

Hello! We're Kooky and Sneaky and we have invited another one of our Shopkins BFFs to our play date. Can you work out who it is?

The Shopkin who has been invited to play is in the grid below. They are the only Shopkin who can be followed in a line from the top of the grid to the bottom of the grid. Draw a line to follow the Shopkin - you may have to go sideways, downwards, upwards or even diagonally!

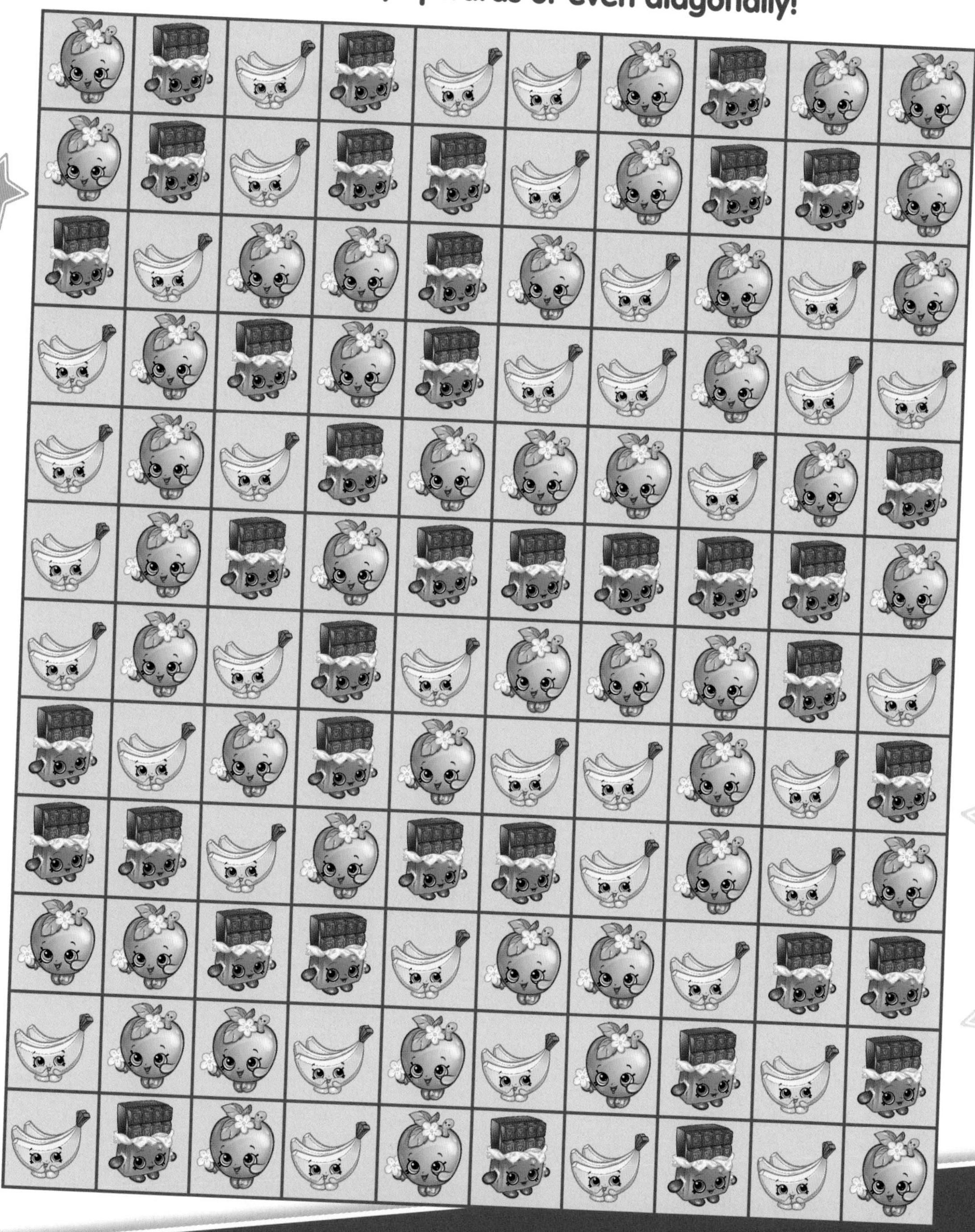

Answers on page 75

THE FRIENDSHIP TIME GAME

This is a two-player game. One player plays as the FRIEND and the other as the GUESSER. If you use a pencil you can rub out and play again and again!

- First the FRIEND must give each Shopkin a time, from 1pm to 4pm, when they are going to meet up. Then cover the times with some scrap paper.
- The GUESSER has to guess what time the FRIEND is meeting each Shopkin! The FRIEND can only meet one Shopkin at each time.
- The GUESSER gets eight guesses to see if they can find the correct time for each Shopkin.
- After each guess, the FRIEND must write in the left-hand column the number of meet-up times the GUESSER has guessed correctly.
- The FRIEND only has to say if a time is in the correct column, they don't have to say which time it is.
- The GUESSER must use the clues after each guess to make a new guess, until they get the correct answer.

SELFIE THE DIFFERENCE

Poppy Corn has been catching up with Miss Pressy, Rainbow Bite and D'lish Donut! Can you spot the BFF selfie that looks different to the main photo?

MAIN PHOTO

BEST FRIENDS PHOTO-EVER!

A

BEST FRIENDS PHOTO-EVER!

B

BEST FRIENDS PHOTO-EVER!

C

BEST FRIENDS PHOTO-EVER!

Spotted the odd selfie out? Now can you find six differences between the odd selfie and the main photo?

Answers on page 75

FRUIT AND FRIENDS

Apple Blossom and Strawberry Kiss are super-sweet best friends! Use the key below and colour them in with your favourite pens!

COLOUR KEY:

1. PERFECT PINK
2. APPLE GREEN
3. LEAFY GREEN
4. JUICY RED
5. PETAL YELLOW
6. WOOD BROWN

BUNCHO'S SQUARES GAME

Hi, I'm Buncho Bananas!
You can play this fun drawing game with your best friend. You and your friend must have different coloured pens. The aim of the game is to complete as many squares as possible to win!

HOW TO PLAY

The youngest player goes first and draws a horizontal or vertical line between two neighbouring dots on the grid. Then, the other player draws a line, and so on. When you draw the line that completes a square, write your initials in the square to claim it as yours! Keep going, taking turns to draw lines between the dots, claiming squares as you complete them. At the end of the game, count the number of squares you have claimed to see who is the winner!

RAINBOW BITE'S MOBILE MATES

Rainbow Bite has created a mobile of her best friends using lots of colourful, cut-out shapes of her besties. Can you match the colourful shapes to her Shopkins friends?

FRIENDSHIP MIX-UP

Coco Nutty is organising a sleepover with all her BFFs, but she's mixed up everyone's names! Can you unscramble the names to reveal the five slumber-party guests?

A LIPPY DONUT

B BUNCHO KISS

C D'LISH LIPS

D POPPY BANANAS

E STRAWBERRY CORN

FRIENDSHIP GROUP SEARCH

Pop! Pop! It's me, Poppy Corn.
Can you help me find all the Shopkins friendship groups in the grid? Also, I'm hiding somewhere in the grid... can you spot me?

A

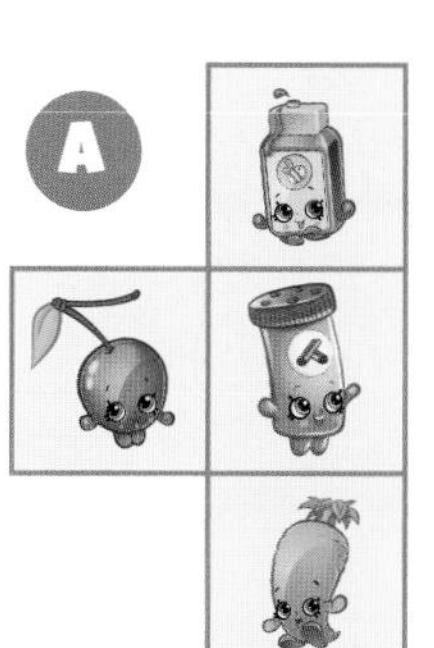

B

C

D

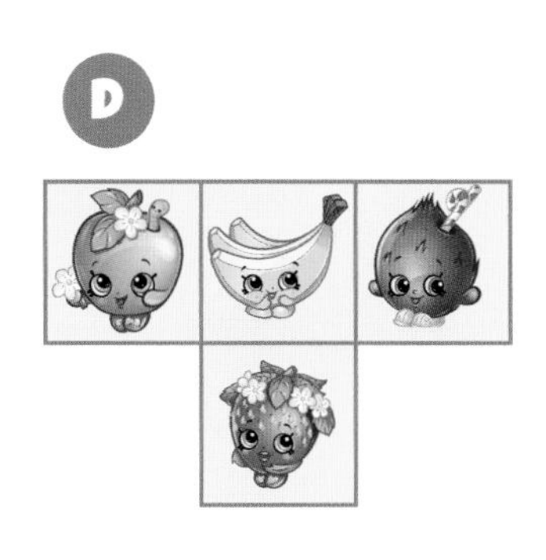

E

F

Answers on page 75

STORY TIME

AIN'T NO PARTY LIKE A SHOPKINS PARTY!

Rainbow Kate had organised a super-sweet party, and every Shopkins who was any Shopkins had turned up. **"Great party,"** said Apple Blossom as she tucked into a tasty cookie. **"But what are we celebrating exactly?"**

Rainbow grabbed a microphone. **"Hi, everybody! I've invited you all here today to plan Jessicake's upcoming BIRTHDAY PARTY!"** She was bursting with ideas. **"What about a costume party? Wait!"** Rainbow's enthusiasm was boiling over. **"Hold the phone everyone… what if we had a surprise party?"**

Lippy Lips silenced Rainbow's excitement and spoke up. **"I think the element of surprise would be hard to pull off."**

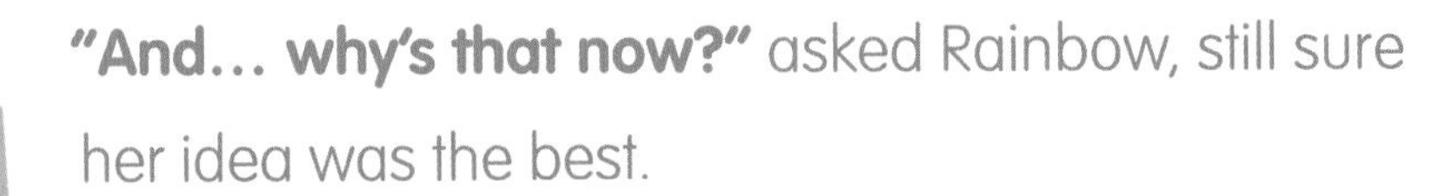

"And… why's that now?" asked Rainbow, still sure her idea was the best.

"Because I'm standing right here," revealed Jessicake as she edged closer to Rainbow.

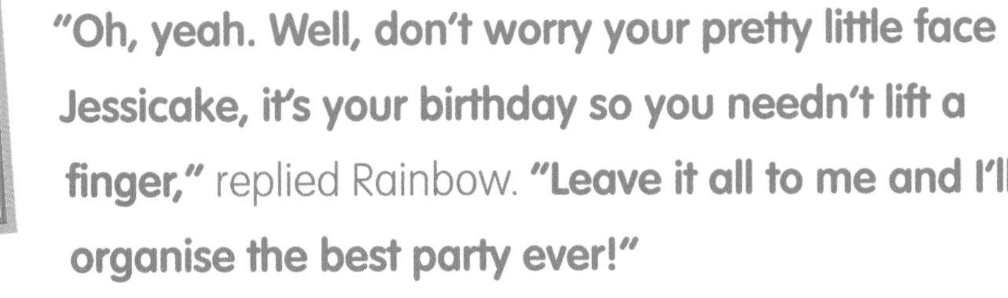

"Oh, yeah. Well, don't worry your pretty little face Jessicake, it's your birthday so you needn't lift a finger," replied Rainbow. **"Leave it all to me and I'll organise the best party ever!"**

The next day was Valentine's Day, but Rainbow didn't have time for love, she was too busy planning Jessicake's party. Rosie Bloom popped into the Small Mart and asked if she could help with the flowers, but Rainbow had all the flowers sorted.

OR SO SHE THOUGHT…

The flowers hadn't arrived! Rainbow grabbed the phone and called the Bouquet Boutique. **"Hi, yes. I'm waiting for a flower delivery,"** she enquired. **"What! You've run out of flowers because of Valentine's Day!"** Rainbow couldn't believe it. **"At least we have the venue sorted."** But then she got a call. **"Oh, no! The venue has been double-booked. I'm going to pop outside for a quick scream."**

As Rainbow panicked, Rosie and the Shopkins decided to help. They needed flowers and somewhere to hold the party. **"I know!"** said Rosie. **"We could have it in the park. There are plenty of flowers there and it's a blooming good place for a party."**

A few days later, Rainbow and Jessicake were tasting food for the big event. CRUNCH! **"Ouch!"** screamed Jessicake as her tooth fell out. **"I'm going to need a crown."** Jessicake rushed to the dentist to sort out her gappy smile.

Rainbow started to panic. Time was running out. She rushed outside and bumped into Tiara Sparkles. **"Rainbow, you appear to be more frazzled than usual,"** said Tiara, concerned.

"Frazzled? I'm fine," said Rainbow, frantically. **"I was supposed to sort out costume ideas three days ago, not to mention the birthday girl needs a new crown! But, hey! I'm totes fine."** Rainbow rushed off looking less than fine and even more frazzled.

"A princess should never celebrate her birthday without a crown," thought Tiara, not realising Rainbow meant a crown for a tooth. **"I know! I'll help Rainbow organise the costumes. We will all be sparkling Princesses."**

FRIENDS FOREVER

STORY TIME

Meanwhile, at the Small Mart, Bridie popped in to see how the party planning was coming along. Rosie told Bridie all about the party and that the venue had changed to the park.

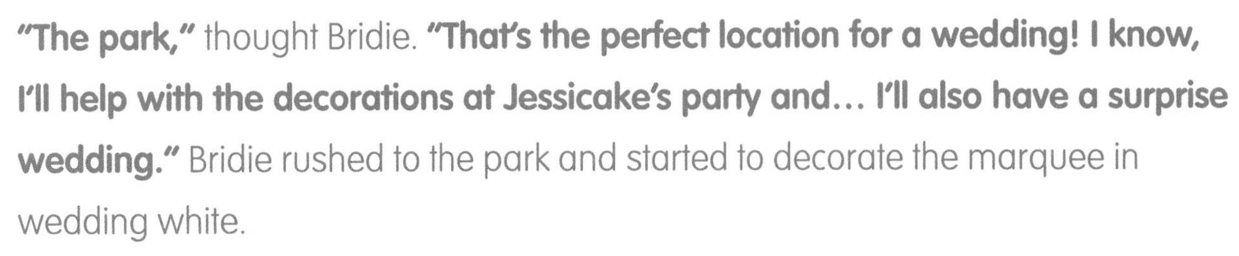

"The park," thought Bridie. **"That's the perfect location for a wedding! I know, I'll help with the decorations at Jessicake's party and… I'll also have a surprise wedding."** Bridie rushed to the park and started to decorate the marquee in wedding white.

Finally, with the flowers, venue, costumes and decorations all sorted, everything was ready for the big day. Rainbow was super-excited and she rushed Jessicake to the party. **"You're going to love this party, birthday girl,"** said Rainbow. **"I've sorted everything!"** She swung open the marquee doors to reveal…

…AN EMPTY ROOM!

"Where is everybody?" shouted Rainbow, upset. She looked around and saw the wedding decorations, the princess theme and all the changes everyone had made to her party plans. **"No! No! No! This is all wrong. This isn't how I wanted the party,"** she said in a temper. **"They are all uninvited!"**

Scenes are from **Ain't no party like a Shopkins party!**

"No, but it is what I wanted," said Jessicake with a smile. **"Everyone has contributed ideas and is doing what they love."**

Rainbow could see Jessicake was happy. **"I'm sorry I didn't listen to you,"** she said. **"If this is what you want then I'm happy too."**

Later, the party was in full swing and everyone was having a super-sweet time. **"Hey, guys,"** said Bridie to Jessicake and Rainbow, as she appeared in her white wedding dress. **"I have something to tell you… I'm getting MARRIED!"**

"Who to?" asked Jessicake and Rainbow.

"Oh… yeah. I thought I had forgotten something. I don't have a groom," replied Bridie a little upset. She wasn't going to have her surprise wedding after all. Then, Jessicake had an idea. There was one more thing that Rainbow could do to make it the perfect party.

Rainbow rushed off and returned with something hidden behind her back. **"Hey, Bridie!"** shouted Rainbow. **"Heads up!"** Rainbow threw Betty Bouquet and Bridie caught her, like it was a bouquet thrown at a real wedding. **"Guys, I caught the bouquet. That means I'm… practically ENGAGED!"** beamed Bridie with delight.

"Thanks Rainbow and everyone," said Jessicake. **"It's been a super-sweet, Shopville-tastic party!"**

NAME TAGS

Jessicake and the Shoppies are styling up their names into cool, creative name tags! Can you help them?

Hi, Shopville fans! It's me Jessicake! Do you want to join me, and my fabulous friends on a friendship day, shopping, dressing up and chilling out?

JESSICAKE

PEPPA-MINT

COCOLETTE

BUBBLEISHA

DONATINA

Why not STYLE UP and design a name tag for your own fabulous name?

BEST FRIEND BADGES

The Shoppies have been making cool, best friend badges of their BFFs, but Bubbleisha has dropped them… oops! Find and count all the different badges for Bubbleisha. She should have 18 badges, does she have them all?

DONATINA'S NEW FRIEND

Donatina has made a new best friend at the Small Mart! Follow the clues below to see which Shopkin is her new BFF!

1. Donatina's new BFF is a food Shopkin.
2. Donatina's new bestie has got green eyes.
3. Donatina's cool new friend has a flower.
4. Donatina's new friend is wearing something pink!

TOASTY POP

D'LISH DONUT

BUNCHO BANANAS

STRAWBERRY KISS

APPLE BLOSSOM

Answers on page 75

FRIENDS FOREVER QUIZ

The Shoppies have a vacancy for a new best friend! Answer the questions below about yourself and see which Shoppie picks you as her bestie.

1 How would you describe your style?

A. Light and airy
B. Delicious and dainty
C. Chilled-out and cool
D. Fabulous and fashion-forward

2 What would be your ideal shopping spree?

A. A burst of bargains and then some bubbly fun
B. A feast of yummy buys and a scrumptious snack
C. Some cool, calm shop-hopping with a scoop of gossip
D. All day, all night and all together!

3 What is your favourite hobby?

A. Fashion
B. Baking
C. Gossiping
D. A, B and C

4 Where would you go for a birthday meal?

A. The Candy Store
B. The Cake Shop
C. The Ice Cream Parlour
D. The Mall Food Court

5 What type of party would you throw?

A. A balloon, bubbly bonanza
B. A scrumptiously stylish soiree
C. A chilled and cool celebration
D. A fabulous friendship festival

MOSTLY As:

Bubbleisha has chosen you as her new BFF! She thinks you have a bubbly sense of humour!

MOSTLY Bs:

Jessicake has picked you as her new bestie! She believes you would make a deliciously fabulous best friend.

MOSTLY Cs:

Peppa-Mint has selected you as her new favourite! She likes your cool and calm personality!

MOSTLY Ds:

It was a tough choice, but all three think you are fab and want to be your friend!

The Shoppies are celebrating their fabulous friendship!
Can you colour them in using your favourite pens?

MALL MAZE

You've gone shopping with the Shoppies, but have lost your way! Enter the Mall Maze and get help from the Shopkins along the route, so you can find your way back to the group!

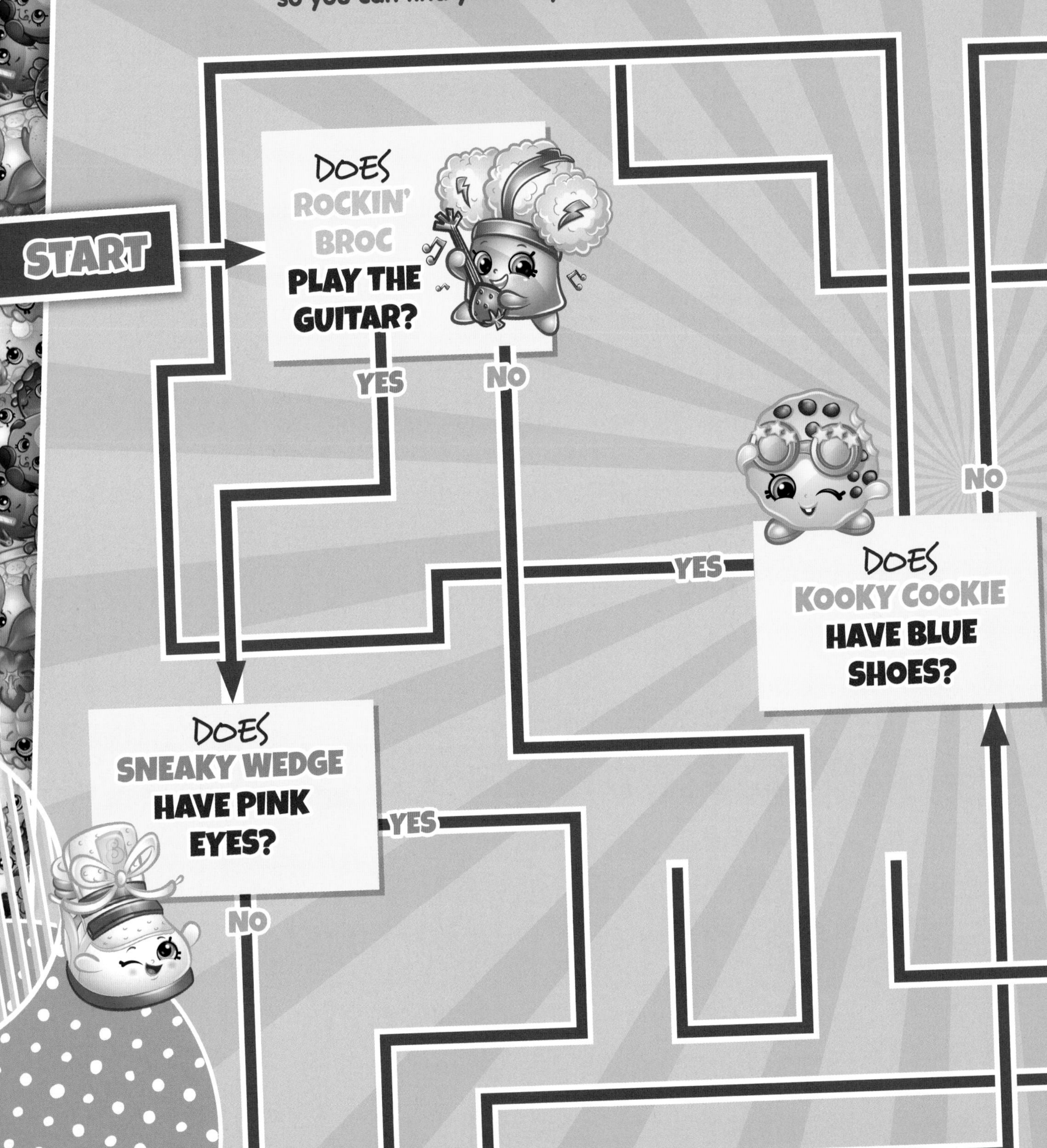

NO
DOES LIPPY LIPS HAVE THREE HEARTS?
YES
YES
IS D'LISH DONUT GREEN?
NO
DOES STRAWBERRY KISS HAVE SIX FLOWERS?
YES
NO
FINISH

COLOUR AND COLLECT

Colour in the blank SPK stickers, then find and count all of Donatina's COOL STICKERS.

Answers on page 75

FRIENDSHIP CALCULATOR

Rainbow Kate has invented an awesome friendship calculator game! Add in the information below, do the maths and find out your friendship rating!

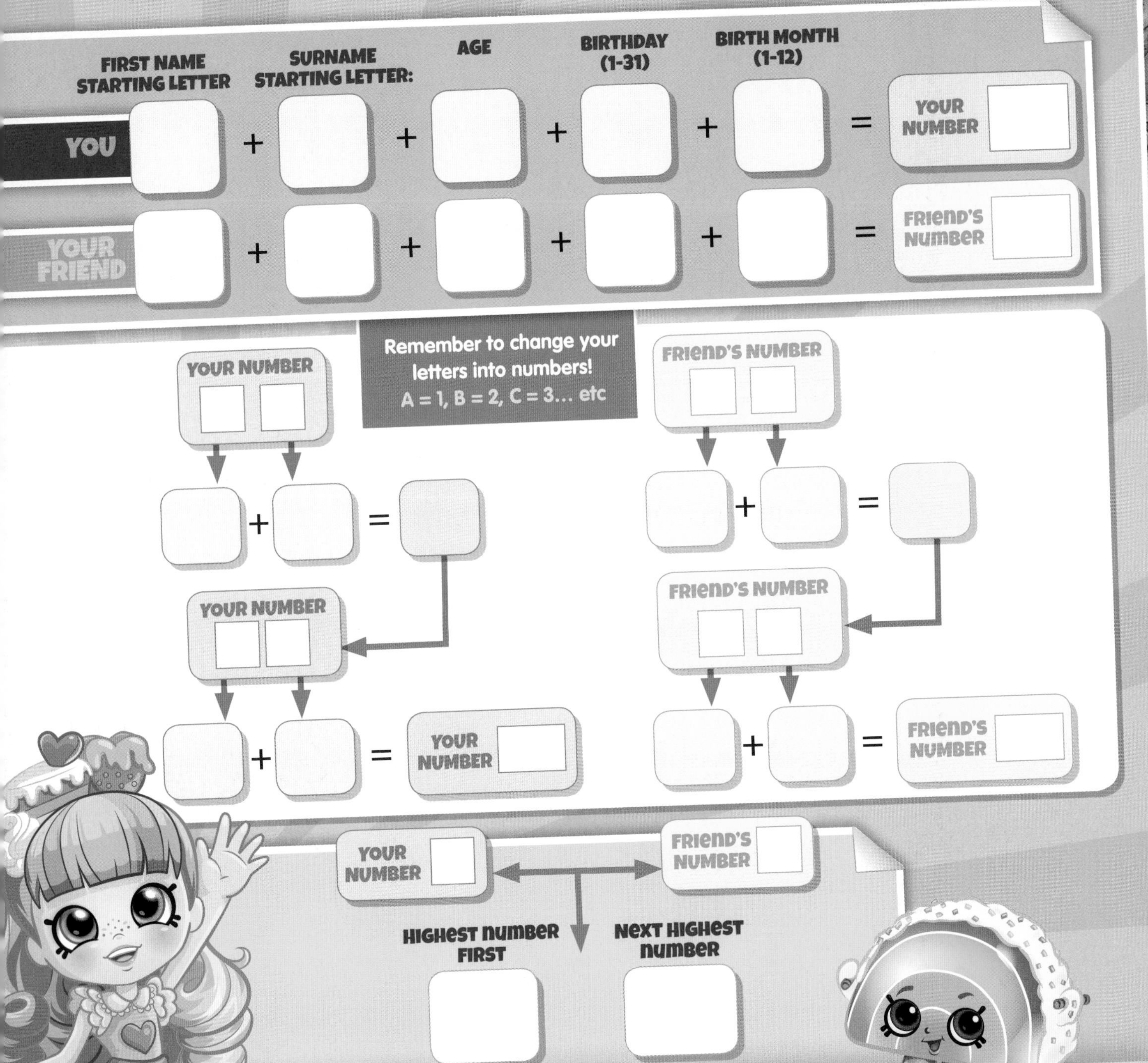

1-20:
NEW FRIENDS
You're getting to know each other and there are lots of fun adventures ahead!

51-75:
STRONG FRIENDS
You have a real bond and a tight friendship

21-50:
FRESH FRIENDSHIP
You really have a bright and exciting friendship that is going places!

76-99:
BEST FRIENDS FOREVER
This is a true friendship and it will last for a long, long time!

CREATE YOUR OWN SHOPPIE

The Shoppies are looking for a new friend to join the Shop Squad. Use the space and instructions below to design and name a new, fabulous Shoppie!

Think of something you love... it could be a food, an item of clothing or an amazing accessory. Then, think of a name that is like the item you've just chosen. Try blending them together or choose one as a first name and the other as a second... voila! You have your Shoppie's new name.

PRETTY POSES

The Shoppies are posing for some cool photos to stick in their friendship diaries. Can you work out which pose Cocolette likes to use the most?

Which Shoppie only uses ONE perfect pose?

SHOPPIES FACTS

How well do you know the Shoppies? Answer the true-or-false statements below to see if you are a Shoppies Super Friend!

1. Donatina hates donuts!

2. Peppa-Mint loves to chill out and gossip!

3. Rainbow Kate's favourite colour is grey!

4. Bubbleisha is bland and boring!

FRIEND OF THE WEEK

The Shoppies have gathered to see who the Shopkins have chosen as Shoppies FRIEND OF THE WEEK! Start with Grand Judge Strawberry Kiss then follow the directions through the grid to see which Shoppie is the winner.

Each Shopkin in the grid stands for a direction. The directions are in the key below. For example, if you land on Kooky Cookie you need to go left.

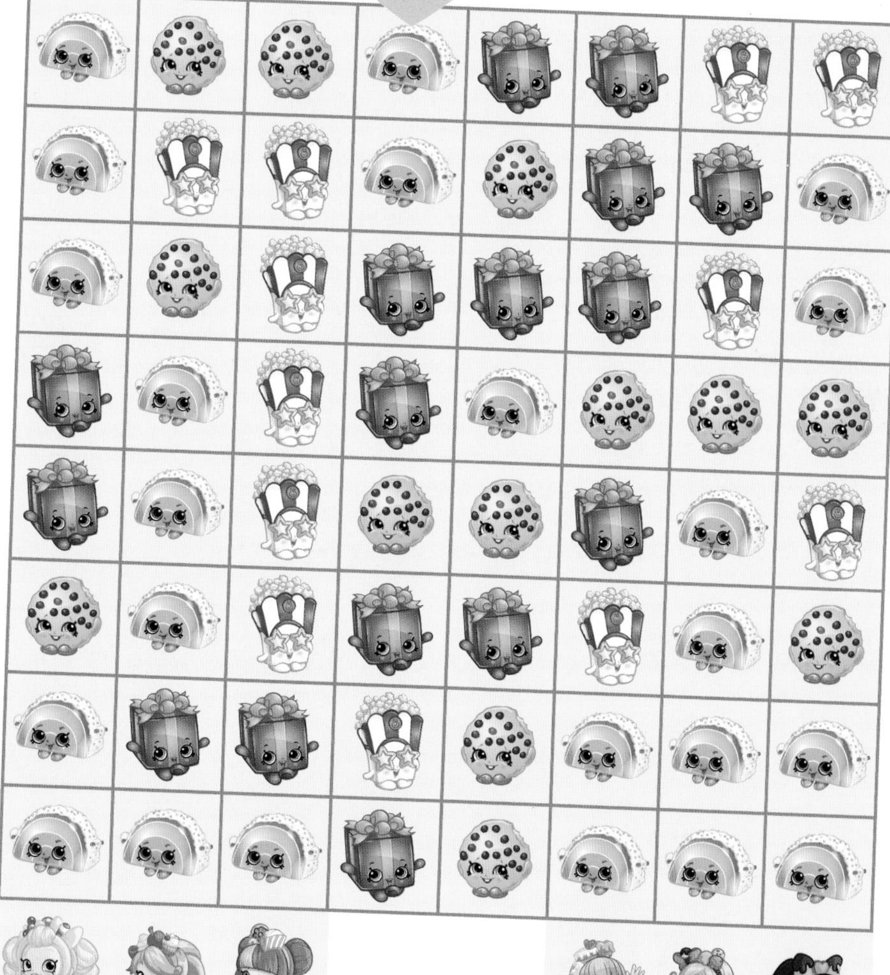

Answers on page 76

STORYBOOK WRITER

Stay cool, everyone!
It's me... Peppa-Mint! I love telling stories, and listening to all the latest gossip. Can you create a story for me in the boxes below? Use the main boxes for your drawings and the lined boxes underneath for your words.

ONCE UPON A TIME IN SHOPVILLE...

SHOPPIES UNITE

... AND THEY ALL LIVED shoppily ever after.

THE RACE TO SMALL MART

The Shoppies are off to see their Shopkins friends at the Small Mart. They've decided to have a race to see who will get there first!

START

1

2
YOU SPOT A BARGAIN AT THE BOUTIQUE! MISS A TURN

3

4

5

6
YOU SWAP YOUR SHOES FOR TRAINERS! ROLL AGAIN

7

8

9

10

11

12
YOU GRAB A TAKEAWAY BOOST JUICE! GO FORWARD 1 SPACE

13

14

15

16
YOU POSE FOR A SELFIE WITH FRIENDS! GO BACK 2 SPACES!

17

18

19

20

YOU WILL NEED:

- 2-6 PLAYERS
- A DICE
- SHOPPIES CHARACTERS

HOW TO PLAY

- Find the counters on your press-out sheet.
- Everyone starts on the Start space.
- The youngest player goes first.
- Roll the dice and move the number of spaces shown on the dice.
- If you land on an instruction space, read it out and follow the actions.
- The winner is the first player to the Finish space.

THE FRIENDSHIP PARADE

Kooky Cookie is organising a Friendship Parade and all her best friends are invited. Can you check Kooky's guest list to see if everyone has turned up?

Which Shopkin is missing?

GUEST LIST

- APPLE BLOSSOM ☐
- BUNCHO BANANAS ☐
- CHEEKY CHOCOLATE ☐
- D'LISH DONUT ☐
- HANDBAG HARRIET ☐
- LIPPY LIPS ☐
- MISS PRESSY ☐
- POPPY CORN ☐
- SNEAKY WEDGE ☐
- RAINBOW BITE ☐
- STRAWBERRY KISS ☐
- SODA POPS ☐
- COCO NUTTY ☐
- CHEEZEY B. ☐
- BREAKY CRUNCH ☐
- SPRINKLE LEE CAKE ☐
- BESSIE BASEBALL ☐
- KAREN CARROT ☐
- CHOC CHIPS ☐
- GINO GELATI ☐

PARADE MAZE

Soda Pops is late for the Friendship Parade! Can you guide Soda Pops through the maze and get her to the parade on time?

START

FINISH

Answers on page 76

BEST FRIEND BALLOONS

The Shopkins have made their own bunches of friendship balloons! Can you match the balloon bunches to each Shopkin?

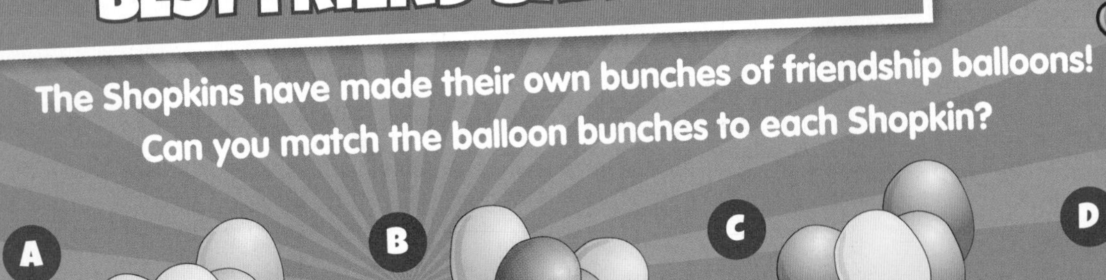

KOOKY COOKIE

DANCE LINES

The Shopkins are having fun dancing at the Friendship Parade! They take turns leading the Dancing Line. Can you work out which Shopkins are missing from the lines below?

PARADE OF COLOUR

All the Shopkins had a super-sweet time hanging out at the Friendship Parade. Use your best pens to complete their day with a burst of colour!

Answers on page 76

BEST FRIEND SELFIE MOBILE

Hi everyone! I'm Rainbow Bite. **Do you want to make a super-sweet, Best Friend Selfie Mobile? Follow my instructions below, and remember: if you need help with cutting and gluing, just ask an adult.**

YOU WILL NEED:

- scissors
- thick card
- glue or sticky tape
- hole punch
- pens or pencils
- photos of your friends
- string or thick cotton

1

Cut a 1 cm (1/2 in) thick strip of card about 40 cm (16 in) long. Bend the card strip into a circle and glue the ends together.

2

Use your hole punch to cut a hole for each friend into the strip of card. Make sure the holes are evenly spread out around the circle.

3

To create your friend mobile phones, cut out a 6 cm x 10 cm (2 $^{1}/_{2}$ in x 4 in) rectangle of card for each best friend. Use your pens or pencils to colour in each rectangle a different colour.

4

In the bottom half of each rectangle draw twelve buttons and number the buttons 0-9. Add a star and hash symbol, so the rectangles now look like mobile phones.

Cut your friend photos into squares, about 5 cm x 5 cm (2 in x 2 in). Make sure you have your friends' faces inside the squares.

Stick the photo squares onto the top of each mobile phone.

Cut out a H-shaped piece of card for each mobile phone, about 3 cm (1 in) long and 2 cm (1/2 in) high.

Cut a piece of string or cotton for each mobile phone. Try different lengths from 15 cm (6 in) to 30 cm (12 in) long.

Tie one end of each string to a H-shaped piece of card.

BEST FRIEND SELFIE MOBILE

Glue each H-shaped piece of card to the back of each mobile phone.

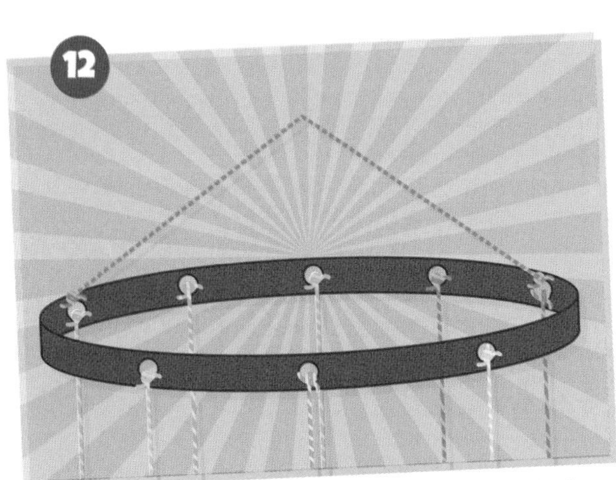

Cut three 20 cm (8 in) pieces of string. Attach the first piece to two opposite holes on the card circle.

Tie the second piece to two opposite holes at right angles to the first.

When the glue is dry, tie the other end of each piece of string to a hole in the card circle.

Liift the cross of string up so the mobile hangs down, and where the support strings cross each other, tie the third piece of string to give you a hanging string which you can stick to your ceiling!

VOILA! YOU HAVE YOUR VERY OWN BEST FRIEND SELFIE MOBILE!

FRIENDSHIP WORDS

Handbag Harriet and Sneaky Wedge are trying to think of lots of friendship words. Can you help them? Search and find the friendship words in the word search.

G	F	I	R	P	B	B	U	D	D	Y	T
D	Q	B	F	W	L	A	C	N	M	Z	H
E	T	E	C	B	G	A	E	H	N	L	P
D	I	Z	V	X	A	I	Y	Q	M	U	I
S	I	Z	A	Y	R	X	H	M	M	K	R
U	T	I	E	F	H	Q	O	W	A	W	E
C	T	E	T	A	S	G	A	A	H	T	B
S	U	S	J	Z	I	E	N	M	D	U	E
H	E	C	W	M	J	A	K	G	X	W	S
B	S	O	A	K	P	N	P	A	L	M	T
X	U	O	W	V	Z	T	D	Y	K	W	I
L	S	O	Y	M	K	H	K	V	N	C	E

BUDDY
BEZZIE
BEST FRIEND
PAL
BESTIE
PLAYMATE
AMIGO

Can you work out the special **EXTRA WORD?** The pink letters are an anagram of a special friendship word...

_ _ _ _ _ _ _ _

PIXEL PALS

Cheeky Chocolate has gone all blocky with her art! Help her colour in her pixel art of her bestie Kooky Cookie.

Why not draw your own pixel-art MASTERPIECE in the space below?

Answers on page 76

MIRROR DIFFERENCES

The Shopkins are posing in front of the mirror as they get ready for a friendship photo shoot! Can you spot the eight differences in the reflection on the other page?

FRIENDSHIP PHOTO SHOOT

The Shopkins have had fun at the photo shoot and they have chosen the best picture. Look at the picture closely and see if you can answer the memory test questions on the next page!

Now, cover the friendship photo on page 52 and see if you can answer the questions below! Remember... no peeking!

1. Which Shopkin is in the middle of the photo?

   ....

2. Who is stood to the right of Kooky Cookie?

   ....

3. How many Shopkins are in the photo?

   ....

4. What colour is Handbag Harriet's bow?

   ....

Answers on page 76

Shopkins™
Once you shop...You can't stop!
MEET THE
WILD STYLE
TRIBES
Wild Style
Color Change Cuties
COLOR CHANGE
Cupcake Chic 9-034
Cupcake Queen 9-035
Cody Coco 9-036
Holly Brolly Cupcake 9-037
Tiny Tops Cake 9-038
Mitzy Oven Mit 9-039
Cupcakes Crumbles 9-040
Polly Cake Pop 9-041
Jemima Cake Timer 9-042
Rainbow Dreamers
RAINBOW
Soda Pops 9-013
Miss Pressy 9-014
Celeste Rainbow Dress 9-015
Elain-Bow Shoe 9-016
Nicole Parasole 9-017
Sunni Brim 9-018
Lottie Lolly Jar 9-019
Rainbow Swirls 9-020
Color Cake
Glamour Gems
GEM
Lippy Lips 9-049
Polly Polish 9-050
Sweetie Scent 9-051
Kissy Kicks 9-052
Rowena Ring Box 9-053
Lippy Zips 9-054
Glitzi Dancers
GLITZI
Tutu Cute 9-022
Tiara 9-023
Polly Pointes 9-024
Little Bow Bella 9-025
Kaila Keyboard 9-026
Shades De'Ballet 9-027
Pamela Camera 9-028
Marabel Music Player 9-029
Missy Makeup Case 9-030
Petite Petals 9-031
Betty Cassette 9-032
Calista Cake 9-033
Flocked 'n' Fluffy
FLUFFY
Candi Cotton 9-043
Cotton Top Cake 9-044
Swirly Shirley 9-045
Fluffy Buffy Shoes 9-046
Cotton Candice Dress 9-047
Flossy Donut 9-048

Glazed Fruits
TRANSLUCENT
Apple Blossom 9-067
Strawberry Kiss 9-068
Nick Fruit Stick 9-069
Stella Citrus Shoe 9-070
Fran Fruit Hat 9-071
Bowla Fruits 9-072
Lemona & Lima 9-073
Zippy Lime Bag 9-074
Melon Minutes 9-075
Patty Pineapple Lamp 9-076
Judy FruitCake 9-077
Bianca Banana 9-078
Frozen Flakes
FROZEN FLAKES
Yo Chi 9-055
Wynter Water Bottle 9-056
Silvia Slushie 9-057
Blockey 9-058
Snug Lee Ski Jacket 9-059
Icy Cool Kids 9-060
Dairy Wrappers
STICKER WRAP
Spilt Milk 9-061
Ghurty 9-062
Audrey Strawberry Milk 9-063
Chester Cheesecake 9-064
Carmen Le Crème 9-065
Melba Milkshake 9-066
OXOX
Heart 'n' Seekers
HIDDEN HEART
Candy Kisses 9-001
Karlee Candy Jar 9-002
Bubble Gum Sweetheart 9-003
Love-Lee Handbag 9-004
Charlotte Heart Cake 9-005
Cutie Compact 9-006
Charmin' Chocolates 9-007
Marcia Heart Mug 9-008
Lovely Hearts Teapot 9-009
Honey Hearts 9-010
Candice Candle 9-011
Primrose Pancakes 9-012
Sweet 'n' Squishy
SQUISHY
Kooky Cookie 9-079
D'LishDonut 9-080
Cheri Choc Chip Bread 9-081
Camile Cream Cookie 9-082
Wanita Waffle 9-083
Cookie Sue Flay 9-084
Martha Choc Chip Muffin 9-085
Lina Loaf 9-086
Bryce Cookie Slice 9-087
Shimmery Unicorn
SHIMMERY
Rainbow Scent 9-088
Starry Unicorn Heels 9-089
PRECIOUS PETPOD SHOPKIN!
Supicorn 9-090
Bling Unicorn Ring 9-091
Rainbow Glow 9-092
Eunice Unicorn Dress 9-093
Common
Rare
Ultra Rare
Special Edition
Limited Edition
Returning Shopkin

MEET THE SHOPPETS

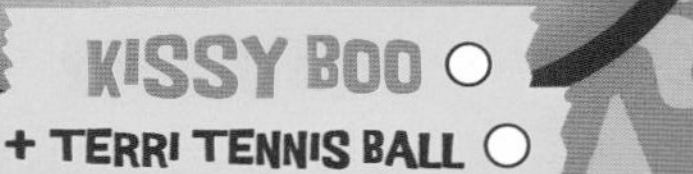

FOXY LEMONS
+ LEONA LEMON TREE
SQUEAK SWEETIE
+ WIZZY WHEEL
SUGAR SWIRL
+ NETTA KNIT
KITTY CRUMBLES
+ CAMILA CAT STAND
SNOW-FRO
+ FLUFFY SNOW BALL
HIP HIP HAMSTER
+ HARRY HAMSTERBALL
AMBEAR BOW
+ BOWDIE BEAR
+ HONEY POTS
DUNCAN
+ COCO ANNA
MELONIE HOPS
+ MELINA SMOOTHIE
LIMITED EDITION
RAINBOW SPARKLE
+ TWI LIGHT CLOUD

MEET THE WILD STYLE SHOPPIES

BELLA BOW
SPECIAL EXCLUSIVE

Bella Bow is one Shoppie who wins ribbons for her bows! She has some serious tying styling! From head to toe there's a pretty bow.

PIPPA MELON
GLAZED FRUITS

Pippa Melon has a Wild Style that's always fresh! She's a natural when it comes to making new friends, and her tribe of Glazed Fruits are extra cute!

VALENTINA HEARTS
HEART 'N' SEEKERS

Wild at heart and a Wild Style to match, Valentina Hearts has a look that everyone loves! Her tribe of "Heart 'n' Seekers" are perfect friends because their love never ends!

CANDY SWEETS
FLOCKED 'N' FLUFFY

With sweet sugary swirls of cotton candy curls, Candy Sweets' Wild Style is buzzing with cuteness! It's no wonder her "Flocked 'n' Fluffy" tribe follows her wherever she goes!

MYSTABELLA
SHIMMERY UNICORN

Mystabella is a Shoppie that everyone dreams about! You can only imagine how much fun she has when she gets together with her fantastic Shimmery Unicorns Tribe!

MIA MILK
DAIRY WRAPPERS

Pure and good, Mia Milk's Wild Style is as fresh as a daisy! She's a smooth mover who likes the simple pleasures of just chillin' with her Shoppet Maisy Moo!

PIROUETTA
GLITZI DANCERS

She's all about grace and glitz. Pirouetta always dresses to impress… nothing is "tutu" cute. Every day is a show, and she likes to practise with her tribe BFFs.

JESSICAKE
COLOR CHANGE CUTIES

Jessicake's a little cutie at heart and likes to pop out and spend the day shopping with her colour-change besties.

PEPPA-MINT
FROZEN FLAKES

It looks like Peppa-Mint is always chilled, but she also has a warm heart. If you have any gossip, her tribe would love the latest scoop!

DONATINA
SWEET 'N' SQUISHY

Donatina has a "hole" lot of fun with her tribe and she is always "round" to have a sweet-and-squishy time.

RAINBOW KATE
RAINBOW DREAMERS

She's colourful in everything she does, wears and eats! Rainbow is a dreamer at heart and cheers up her friends with some rainbow therapy!

LIPPY LULU
GLAMOUR GEMS

She's always "pout" and about with her glamorous besties! Lippy is glossy, bossy and a gem of a friend!

WHICH TRIBE?

There are some new tribes in town!
Can you match the clues to the new Shopkins Friendship Tribes?

1. WE LOVE A BURST OF COLOUR AND OUR HEADS ARE ALWAYS IN THE CLOUDS!
2. WE HAVE A MYTHICAL GLIMMER TO OUR GROUP STYLE!
3. WE LIKE TO CHILL OUT AND PLAY IT COOL... NO FLAKING OUT!

A 

SHIMMERY UNICORN

B 

C 

GLAMOROUS GRID DRAW

Hi, Wild Style fans!
I'm Kissy Boo and I belong to the Glamour Gems tribe! Can you copy and draw me in the grid? Use the grid lines to help!

TRIBAL TANGLE

Oh, no! What a mix-up! Can you help join the tribes together? Start at the tribe's name and follow the lines to join the three members of each tribe.

LOST IN A CROWD

It's a busy day in Shopville and the friendship tribes have been split up! Can you pair the Shopkins with another member of their tribe?

Answers on page 76-77

COLOR CHANGE CUTIES

Meet the Color Change Cuties! Can you colour them in?

TRIBE SEARCH

How well do you know the new Wild Style tribes? Search the grid and find each tribe group below.

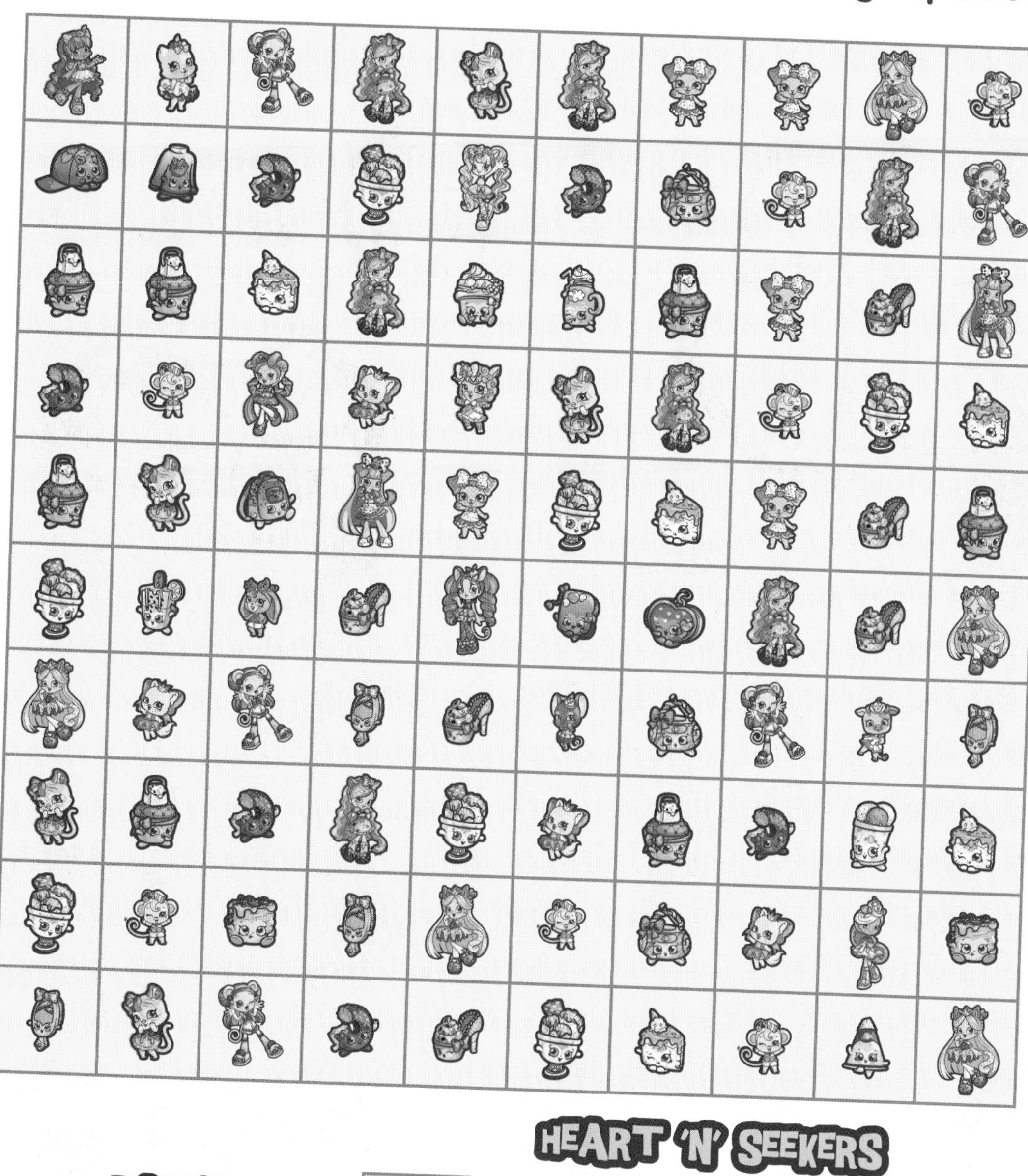

HEART 'N' SEEKERS

DAIRY WRAPPERS

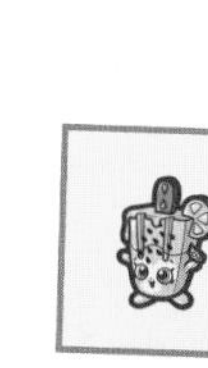

GLAZED FRUITS

FLOCKED 'N' FLUFFY

GLAMOUR GEMS

Answers on page 77

WHICH TRIBE ARE YOU?

Which tribe is your home from home? Which group of glamorous goodies fits your flair, fashion and wild style? Answer the yes-or-no questions below and see which tribe suits you!

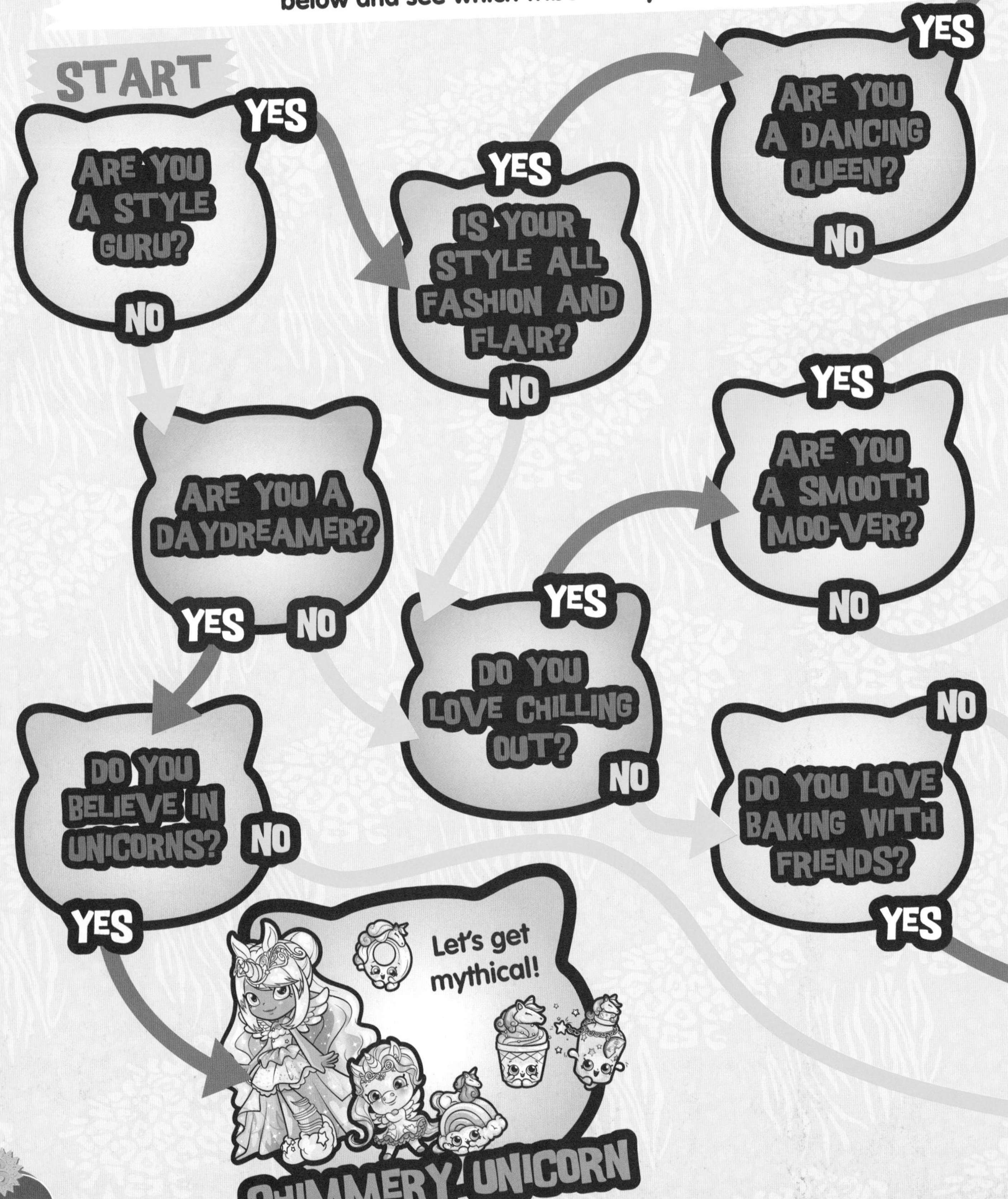

Welcome to the glamour gang!
GLAMOUR GEMS

Let's be the best boogie friends ever!
GLITZI DANCERS

Smooth by name, smooth by nature!
DAIRY WRAPPERS

We're all about playing it cool!
FROZEN FLAKES

We're baking to meet you!
COLOR CHANGE CUTIES

Join our sweet and scrummy tribe!
SWEET 'N' SQUISHY

You're a dream member of our tribe!
RAINBOW DREAMERS

CHILL OUT AND COLOUR IN

USE YOUR FAVOURITE PENS TO COLOUR IN THE COOL GANG!

TRIBE TALKING

The tribes love to send special messages to each other. Use your press-out WILD STYLE CODE WHEEL to decode the messages below. Skip to page 72 to see how to put your press-out code wheel together... then remember to come back!

CODEBREAKER TIP: REMEMBER TO USE THE CORRECT TRIBE ICON KEY SO YOUR CODE WHEEL IS SET TO THE CORRECT CODE LETTERS!

TRIBE ICON KEY

,L SV#L !V ,OPYS
HUK !,PYSD

___ ______ ___
_______ _____
____

TRIBE ICON KEY

JU JT BMM BCPVU
GBTIJPOA GMBJS BOE IBJS?

___ ___ ____ _______
__________ ______
____ _______

TRIBE ICON KEY

LX TGX UT,?CZ ?I
!TEEXCP

___ ____
________ ___
____

PHOTO BOOTH SNAPS

Candy Sweets has taken some yummy photos of her friendship tribe besties! Can you work out which close-ups belong to the photo strip? Which close-up isn't part of the pictures?

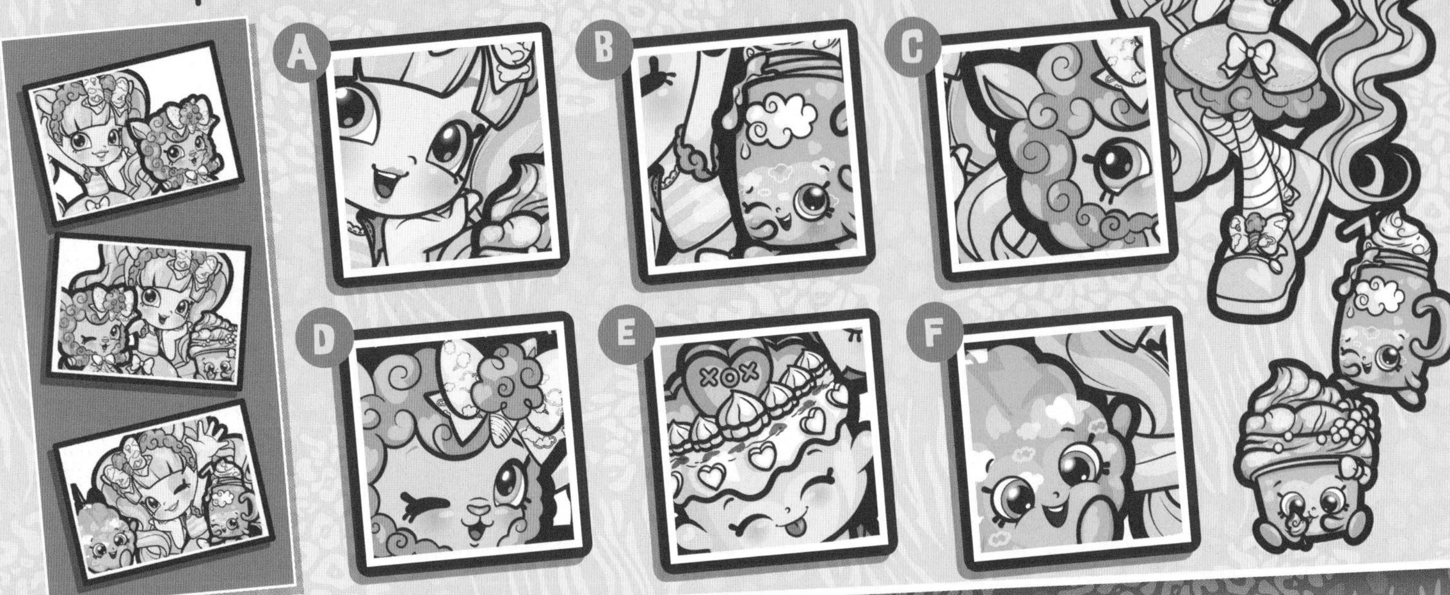

RAINBOW DOTS

Hello, my colourful chums! I'm Rainbow Kate! **Join up all my colourful dots and then colour me in.**

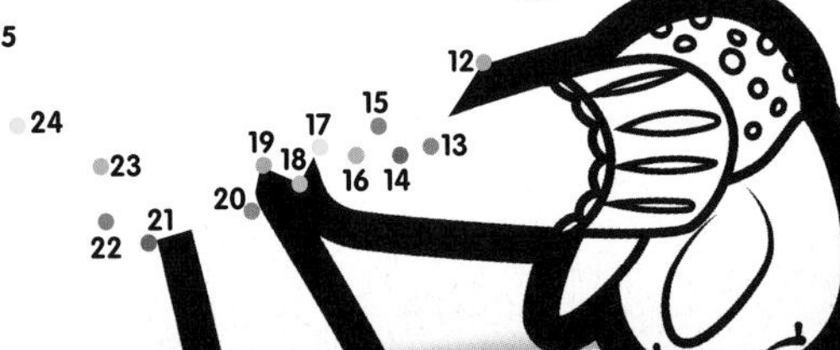

IN THE SPOTLIGHT

The new tribes have become quite the celebrities in Shopville! Can you match the spotlight shadows with the tribe groups?

NEW SHOPPIE IN TOWN

Who's this fabulous fashionista with a heart of sweetness? Cross out the pairs of letters and use the remaining letters to complete her name!

Answers on page 75

NAME THAT TRIBE

Are you a Shopkins Wild Style fan? See if you can un-muddle these tribe names. Which name doesn't belong to any of the tribes?

A GLAZED GEMS

B FROZEN DREAMERS

C RAINBOW FRUITS

D GLAMOUR FLAKES

E FASHION STARS

TRIBAL TABLES

Jessicake and the Color Change Cuties need help completing this Tribal Table! Each row and column can only contain a certain number of icons. Read the number of icons that should be in each column and row, and draw in the missing icons.

PIPPA PUZZLE

Pippa Melon has snapped some super-smart photos of her Glazed Fruits BFFs. Can you complete the two puzzle pictures? Which piece doesn't belong to either of the puzzle pictures?

Answers on page 77

THE NAME GAME

Donatina and Candy Sweets are trying to complete the fun Name Game puzzle. Can you help them match the groups of missing letters to the gaps in the crossword, and complete the Shoppets' names?

MISSING LETTER GROUPS

1	U	P	K
2	S	Y	B
3	X	Y	L
4	D	U	N
5	S	W	I
6	E	A	R
7	A	K	E

WILD STYLE MEMORIES

Valentina Hearts has made a photo-memory book of all the wild times she has spent with her friends. Can you find and count all the items in the list below?

HOW MANY CAN YOU SPOT?

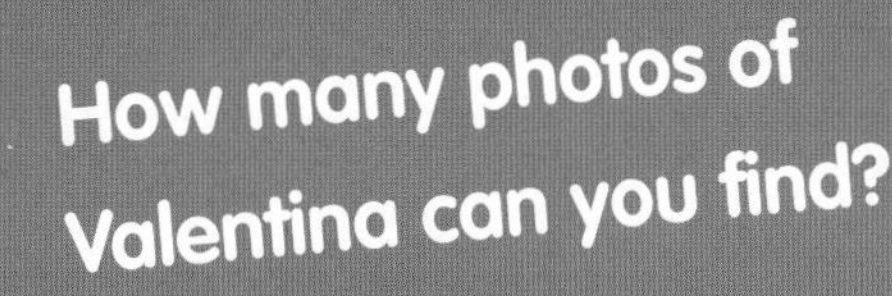

How many photos of Valentina can you find?

Can you spot Squeak Sweetie?

Answers on page 77

CHECK YA LATER!

We hope you had a scrumptiously, super-sweet time in SHOPVILLE!

We've loved hanging out and have had a HOLE load of fun!

Thanks for spending time with us and we hope we've proved to be a wild BUNCH of Shopkins!

Remember to come and see us again soon... we love GIVING you our time and affections!

And remember, once you SHOP... you can't STOP!

ANSWERS

Here are all the answers to the fantastic puzzles! Check them out to see if you were right!

TOASTY POP is on page 25, CHEE ZEE is on page 11, BREAKY CRUNCH is on page 42, ROCKIN' BROC is on page 28, NUTTY BUTTER is on page 75.

PAGE 8
BESTIES PAIR-UP GAME:
SODA POPS and CHEEZEY B., LIPPY LIPS and KAY CUPCAKE, BUNCHO BANANAS and PIPPA LEMON, RAINBOW BITE and APPLE BLOSSOM.

CHEEKY'S NEW BFF:
WAFER TOPS.

PAGE 9
DANCE PARTNERS:
A – SODA POPS danced with APPLE BLOSSOM, B – LIPPY LIPS danced with PIPPA LEMON, C – BUNCHO BANANAS danced with CHEEZEY B..

PARTY BAG TANGLE:
APPLE BLOSSOM – bag A, LIPPY LIPS – bag B, CHEEKY CHOCOLATE – bag C, RAINBOW BITE – bag D.

PAGE 11
CHATTER-PHONES:
CHILLI PEPPA is phoning BUNCHO BANANAS, RUNNY HONEY is phoning HANDBAG HARRIET, MEL T MOMENT is phoning STRAWBERRY KISS, BESSY BASEBALL is phoning COCO NUTTY, GROOVY GLASSES is phoning CHEEZEY B..

PAGE 12
WHICH KOOKY?:
C.

THE GUESS ME GAME:
D'LISH DONUT.

PAGE 13
WHO'S COMING TO PLAY?:

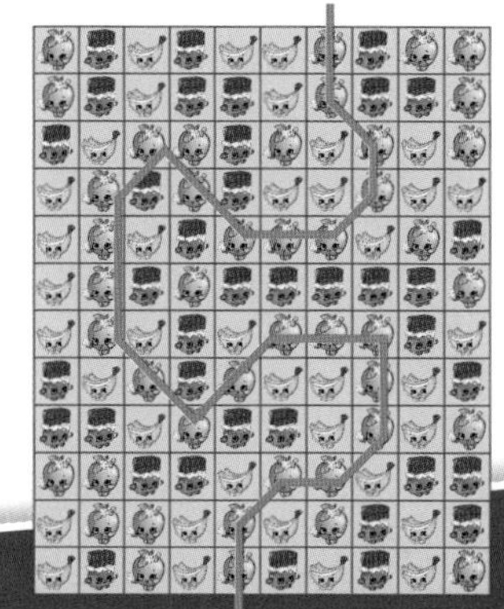

APPLE BLOSSOM is coming to play.

PAGE 15
SELFIE THE DIFFERENCE:
SELFIE C.

PAGE 18
RAINBOW BITE'S MOBILE MATES:
A – 4, B – 3, C – 1, D – 2, E – 5.

FRIENDSHIP MIX-UP:
LIPPY LIPS, BUNCHO BANANAS, D'LISH DONUT, POPPY CORN, STRAWBERRY KISS.

PAGE 19
FRIENDSHIP GROUP SEARCH:

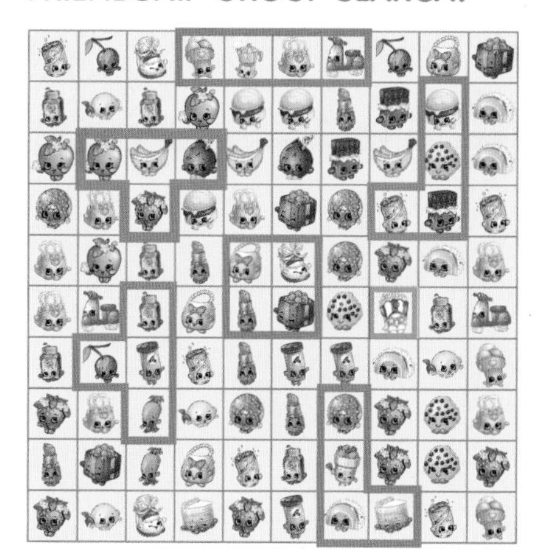

PAGE 25
BEST FRIEND BADGES:
JESSICAKE = 3, BUBBLEISHA = 4, RAINBOW KATE = 2, COCOLETTE = 4, PEPPA-MINT = 3, DONATINA = 2

DONATINA'S NEW FRIEND:
APPLE BLOSSOM.

PAGES 30-31
COLOUR AND COLLECT:

PAGE 34
PRETTY POSES:
COCOLETTE likes pose C the most.

DONATINA only uses one perfect pose.

SHOPPIES FACTS:
1 - False, 2 - True, 3 - False, 4 - False.

PAGE 35
FRIEND OF THE WEEK:

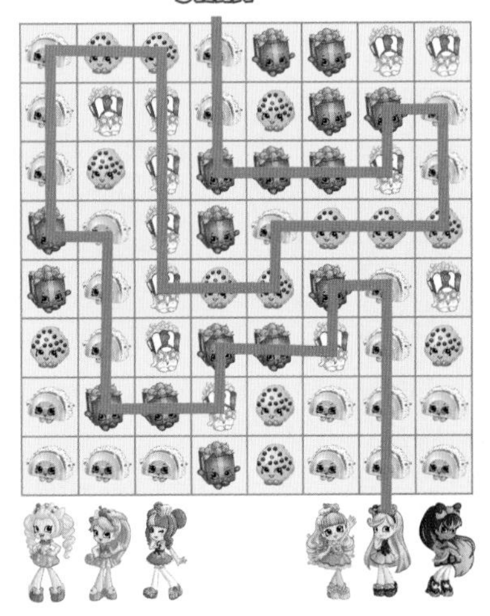

PAGE 42
THE FRIENDSHIP PARADE:
SODA POPS is missing.

PAGE 43
PARADE MAZE:

PAGE 44
BEST FRIEND BALLOONS:
A – APPLE BLOSSOM, B – KOOKY COOKIE, C – STRAWBERRY KISS, D – RAINBOW BITE.

DANCE LINES:

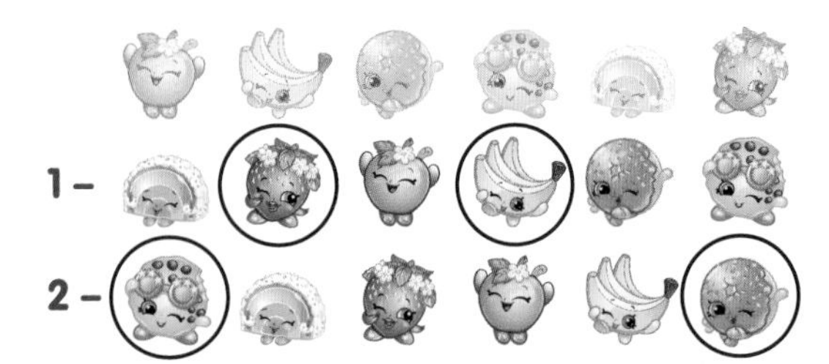

PAGE 50
FRIENDSHIP WORDS:

G	F	I	R	P	B	B	U	D	D	Y	T
D	Q	B	F	W	L	A	C	N	M	Z	H
E	T	E	C	B	G	A	E	H	N	L	P
D	I	Z	V	X	A	I	Y	Q	M	U	I
S	I	Z	A	Y	R	X	H	M	M	K	R
U	T	I	E	F	H	Q	O	W	A	W	E
C	T	E	T	A	S	G	A	A	H	T	B
S	U	S	J	Z	I	E	N	M	D	U	E
H	E	C	W	M	J	A	K	G	X	W	S
B	S	O	A	K	P	N	P	A	L	M	T
X	U	O	W	V	Z	T	D	Y	K	W	I
L	S	O	Y	M	K	H	K	V	N	C	E

The special word is: SOULMATE.

PAGES 52-53
MIRROR DIFFERENCES:

FRIENDSHIP PHOTO SHOOT:
1 - RAINBOW BITE, 2 – D'LISH DONUT, 3 – 12, 4 – PINK.

PAGE 60
WHICH TRIBE?
1 – C, 2 – A, 3 – B.

PAGE 61
TRIBAL TANGLE:

SWEET 'N' SQUISHY

HEART 'N' SEEKERS

GLITZI DANCERS

LOST IN A CROWD:
CUPCAKE FASHIONISTA and CELINE CUPCAKE SHOE, BOWLA FRUITS and BIANCA BANANA, LIPPY LIPS and POLLY POLISH, SWEETIE SIPS and CANDI COTTON.

PAGE 63
TRIBE SEARCH:

PAGE 67
TRIBE TALKING:
GLITZI DANCERS – We love to whirl and twirl!, GLAMOUR GEMS – It is all about fashion, flair and hair!, COLOR CHANGE CUTIES – We are baking it happen!.

PAGE 68
PHOTO BOOTH SNAPS:
Close-up E is not from the photo strip.

PAGE 69
IN THE SPOTLIGHT:
A – GLAZED FRUITS, B – DAIRY WRAPPERS, C – SWEET 'N' SQUISHY, D – SHIMMERY UNICORN.

NEW SHOPPIE IN TOWN:
VALENTINA HEARTS.

PAGE 70
NAME THAT TRIBE:
GLAZED FRUITS, FROZEN FLAKES, RAINBOW DREAMERS, GLAMOUR GEMS. FASHION STARS is not a tribe name.

TRIBAL TABLES:

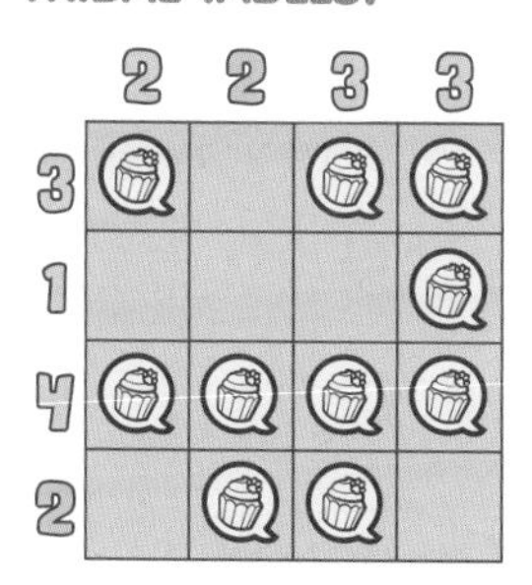

PAGE 71
PIPPA PUZZLE:

Piece G doesn't belong to the jigsaw pictures.

PAGE 72
THE NAME GAME:

PUPKINCAKE
SUGARSWIRL
KISSYBOO
FOXYLEMONS
BUNNYBOW
BOWDIEBEAR
DUNCAN

PAGE 73
WILD STYLE MEMORIES:

There are 4 photos of VALENTINA. SQUEAK SWEETIE is in the bottom-right photo.

SPK!
Ask an adult to help you cut out the posters on the next pages.

WE ARE SPK!

S
Sweet 'N
BUBBLY

SPK!

Yeah!

LOVE WHO YOU ARE

NEVER
ENDING
FUN!
S

JUST BE YOU!

Cheeky

Super sweet

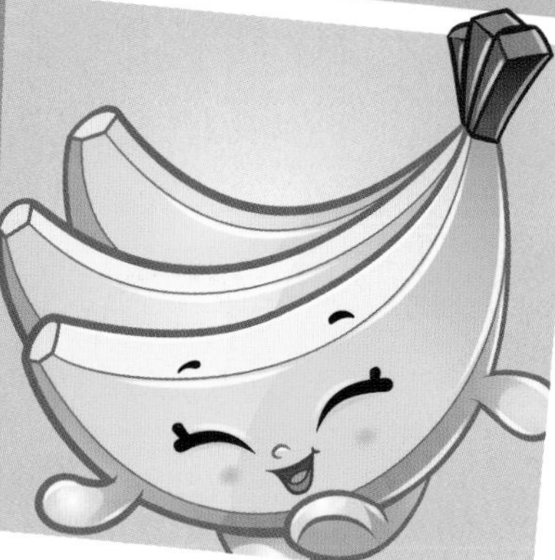
Bunch of fun!

Fabulous

Style icon

Always happy

Smart

Cool

SPK UNITE

WE
ARE
SPK

WE ARE

AWESOME!

S
BETTER
Together

BETTER Together

WE ARE SPK!

NEVER
ENDING
FUN!
S

S

Love
SPK!

SPK!

Bunch of fun!
Cool
Always happy
Style icon
Super sweet
Cheeky
Smart
Style icon
Fabulous